How to use this book

Follow the advice, in italics, given for you on each page.
Support the children as they read the text that is shaded in cream.
***Praise** the children at every step!*

Detailed guidance is provided in the Read Write Inc. Phonics Handbook.

8 reading activities

Children:
- *Practise reading the speed sounds.*
- *Read the green, red and challenge words for the story.*
- *Listen as you read the introduction.*
- *Discuss the vocabulary check with you.*
- *Read the story.*
- *Re-read the story and discuss the 'questions to talk about'.*
- *Re-read the story with fluency and expression.*
- *Practise reading the speed words.*

Speed sounds

Consonants *Say the pure sounds (do not add 'uh').*

f ff	l (ll)	m mm	n nn kn	r rr	s ss ce	v ve	z zz s	(sh)	th	ng nk

b bb	c k ck	d dd	g gg	h	j	p pp	qu	t tt	w (wh)	x	y	ch tch

Vowels *Say the vowel sound and then the word, eg 'a', 'at'.*

at	hen head	in	on	up	day	see happy	high	blow

zoo	look	car	for	fair	whirl	shout	boy

*Each box contains one sound but sometimes more than one grapheme. Focus graphemes are **circled**.*

Green words

Read in Fred Talk (pure sounds).

st<u>ay</u>   h<u>ay</u>   aw<u>ay</u>   daft   pond   tro<u>ll</u>   spla<u>sh</u>   wi<u>ll</u>   not

Read the root word first and then with the ending.

s<u>ay</u> → s<u>ay</u>s   jump → jumps

ye<u>ll</u> → ye<u>ll</u>s   l<u>oo</u>k → l<u>oo</u>ks

Red words

<u>the</u>   <u>you</u>   <u>wh</u>at   <u>I'll</u>   to   was   he   go

5

Vocabulary check

Discuss the meaning (as used in the story) after the children have read the word.

definition:

troll   *a kind of monster*

Punctuation to note in this story:

Trog Fay	*Capital letters for names*
He Run The	*Capital letters that start sentences*
.	*Full stop at the end of each sentence*
!	*Exclamation mark used to show surprise*

The troll in the pond

Introduction

Do you know what your reflection is? It's when you see yourself when you look in a mirror or on water.

Fay, the girl in this story, wants Trog the troll to go away. So she tries to frighten him by telling him that there's a big troll in the pond.

When Trog looks in the pond what do you think he sees? Let's find out.

Story written by Cynthia Rider
Illustrated by Tim Archbold

Trog the troll is in the hay.

He will not go
away and says
he will stay.

"Run away, Trog," says Fay.

"The big troll in the pond will get you if you stay."

"What big troll?" yells Trog.

Trog looks in

the pond.

A big troll looks

back at him.

"I'll bash you to bits,"

yells Trog.

"I'll bash you to bits,"

yells the big troll.

"I'll get that troll," yells Trog.

Splash! He jumps in the pond.

"Daft Trog!" says Fay. "The big troll

in the pond was you!"

Questions to talk about

Re-read the page. Read the question to the children. Tell them whether it is a **FIND IT** question or **PROVE IT** question.

FIND IT

✓ Turn to the page

✓ Read the question

✓ Find the answer

PROVE IT

✓ Turn to the page

✓ Read the question

✓ Find your evidence

✓ Explain why

Page 8:   FIND IT   *What does Trog say he will do?*

Page 9-10:   PROVE IT   *How does Fay trick Trog?*

Page 11:   PROVE IT   *Do you think Trog likes the 'other' Troll? Why?/Why not?*

Page 12:   FIND IT   *What does Trog say he is going to do?*

Page 13:   PROVE IT   *What does Fay think of Trog?*